Freddie Farquar's

'Naughty but Nice!'

Ballad of Eskimo Nell

This (very valuable) First Edition of Freddie
Farquar's 'Naughty but Nice!' Series published 1998 by
The Dog's Rollocks Ideas Co Ltd.,
96/98 Camden Mews, London NW1 9AG.
Tel: +44 (0) 171 482 5151, Fax: +44 (0) 171 267 8837.

Distributed by Appletree Press Ltd.,
19-21 Alfred Street, Belfast BT2 8DL.
Tel: +44 (0) 1232 243074, Fax: +44 (0) 1232 246756.

Printed in EU

The Ballad of Eskimo Nell

A catalogue record for this book is available
from the British Library.

ISBN 0 9533582 0 8

9 8 7 6 5 4 3 2 1

Dedicated to Thomas Lauredemmy
(collectively, you know who you are)

Foreword

"I have been inordinately fond of the Ballad of Eskimo Nell ever since the days when my mad Australian friend Bruce would empty tea rooms and coffee houses with his drunken and rambling rendition.

Under the alfluence of incohol its 50-plus verses are memorably funny. Sober, they are exquisitely clever and rude.

The Ballad of Eskimo Nell was reputedly written in the early years of this century, of Australian origin (although the lines 'Have you ever seen the pistons of the mighty CPR?' could be taken to suggest the Canadian Pacific Railway). No-one seems to know who penned it.

In the interests of young children's moral standing, and maiden aunts' susceptibilities, we have made just three changes to the text, where the Saxon expletives starting with 'f' and 'c' have been left doing just that, and a certain substance has been given the name of toffee (although clever readers will no doubt spot the word that rhymes with the changed one).

I would hope you would all join me in wishing the thanks of a grateful nation to our strawberry farming friend in Kent for this version of the epic ode."

When a man grows old and his balls go cold,
And the tip of his prick turns blue.
And it bends in the middle like a one-stringed fiddle,
I'll tell you a tale or two.

So pull up a chair, stand me a drink,
And a tale to you I'll tell.
Of Dead Eye Dick and Mexico Pete
And a harlot called Eskimo Nell.

When Dead Eye Dick and
Mexico Pete
Go forth in search of fun.
It's Dead Eye Dick that slings the
prick,
And Mexico Pete the gun.

When Dead Eye Dick and
Mexico Pete
Are sore depressed and sad.
It's always a c●●● that bears the
brunt,
But the shootin' ain't so bad!

Now Dead Eye Dick and
  Mexico Pete
Lived down by Dead Man's
  Creek.
And such was their luck they'd
  had no f●●●,
For nigh on half a week.

Just a moose or two and a
  caribou,
And a bison cow or so.
But to Dead Eye Dick with
  his king-size prick,
This f●●●ing was mighty
  slow.

To do or dare, this horny pair,
    Set forth for the Rio Grande.
Dead Eye Dick with his mighty
    prick,
And Pete with his gun in his hand.

Now as they blazed their noisy
   trail,
No man their path withstood.
And many a bride, her husband's
   pride,
Knew pregnant widowhood.

They reached the strand of the
   Rio Grande,
At the height of the blazing noon.
And to slake their thirst and do
   their worst,
They sought Black Mike's Saloon.

As they pushed the swing
   doors open wide,
Both prick and gun flashed free.
"According to sex, you bleeding
   wrecks,
You drinks or f●●●s with me!"

Now they'd heard the name of
Dead Eye Dick,
From the Maine to the Panama.
As with nothing worse than a
muttered curse,
Those Dagos sought the bar.

The girls too knew his playful ways,
Down on the Rio Grande.
So forty whores dropped forty drawers
At Dead Eye Dick's command!

They saw the fingers of Mexic Pete,
Itch on the trigger grip.
They didn't wait: at a fearful rate,
Those whores began to strip.

Now Dead Eye Dick was breathing quick,
    breathing quick,
With lecherous snorts and
    grunts.
As forty bums were bare to view,
So likewise forty c●●●s!

Now forty bums and forty c●●●s,
    If you'll just use your wits.
And if you're slick on arithmetic,
That's likewise eighty tits!

Now eighty tits are a gladsome
    sight,
To a man with a raging stand!
It may be rare in Berkeley
    Square,
But not on the Rio Grande.

Now Dead Eye Dick had f●●●ed a few,
On the last preceeding night.
But this was only done for fun,
Just to whet his appetite.

His phallic limb was in f●●●ing trim,
As he backed and took a run.
He made a dart for the nearest tart,
And scored a hole in one!

He bore her to the dusty floor,
   And there he f●●●ed her fine.
And though she grinned, it put the
   wind
Up the other thirty nine!

When Dead Eye Dick lets
loose his prick,
He's got no time to spare.
For speed and strength, combined
with length,
He fairly singes hair!

He made a dart at the next spare tart,
When into that Harlots' Hell,
Strolled a gentle maid who was
    unafraid,
And her name was Eskimo Nell.

By this time Dick had got his
    prick,
Well into number two.
When Eskimo Nell let out a
    yell,
She bawled at him "Hey, you!"

He gave a flick of his muscular
    prick,
And the whore shot over his head.
He wheeled about with an angry
    shout,
Both face and prick were red.

She glanced out hero up and
   down,
His looks she did decry.
With utter scorn she glimpsed the
   horn,
That rise from his hairy thigh.

She blew the smoke from her
    cigarette,
Over his steaming nob.
So utterly beat was Mexico Pete,
That he failed to do his job.

It was Eskimo Nell who broke
    the spell,
In accents clear and cool:
"You c••• struck shrimp of a
    Yankee pimp,
You call that thing a tool?"

"If this here town can't take that down,"
She sneered at the cowering whores.
"Then there's one little c●●● that can do the stunt:
It's Eskimo Nell's, not yours!"

She stripped her garments, one by one,
With an air of conscious pride.
And as she stood in her womanhood,
They saw her great divide.

She seated herself on a table top,
Where someone had left a glass.
With a twitch of her tits, she crushed it to bits,
Between the cheeks of her arse!

She flexed her knees with supple
    ease,
And spread her legs apart.
With a friendly nod to the mangy
    sod,
She gave him his cue to start.

Ｂut Dead Eye Dick knew a
    trick or two,
And meant to take his time.
For a gal like this was f●●●ing
    bliss,
So he played a pantomime.

He flexed his arsehole to and fro,
   And made his balls inflate.
Until they looked like granite nobs
On top of a garden gate!

He blew his anus inside out,
   His balls increased in size.
His mighty prick grew twice as
   thick,
And stretched up past his eyes.

He polished it with alcohol,
     And made it steaming hot.
To finish the job he sprinkled his
     nob
With a cayenne pepper pot.

Then neither did he take a run,
     Nor did he take a leap.
Nor did he stoop but took a
     swoop,
And a steady forward creep.

With piercing eye he took a
  sight,
Along his mighty tool.
The steady grin as he pushed it in
Was calculated cool.

Have you seen the mighty pistons
On the giant CPR?
With the grinding force of a
thousand horse,
Well, you know what pistons are!

Or you think you do, but you've
yet to learn,
The ins and outs of the trick.
Of the work that's done on a
non-stop run,
By a guy like Dead Eye Dick!

But Eskimo Nell was no infidel
   But as good as a whole hareem.
With the iron strength of her
   abdomen,
And the Rock of Ages between.

Amid thrusts she could take the
   stream
Like the flush of a water closet.
And she gripped his cock like the
   Chatswood Lock,
On the National Safe Deposit!

But Dead Eye Dick would not
     come quick,
He meant to conserve his powers.
For he'd a mind to grind and grind
For a couple of solid hours.

Nell laid for a while with a subtle
     smile,
The grip of her c●●● grew keener.
With a flick of her thigh she sucked
     him dry
With the ease of a vacuum cleaner!

She performed this trick in a way
    so slick,
As to set in complete defiance,
The basic laws and primary cause
That govern sexual science!

She calmly rode through the
   phallic code,
That for years had stood the test.
And the ancient rules of the classic
   schools
In a second or two went West!

And so, my friend, we near the
	end,
Of copulation's epic.
The effect on Dick was sudden
	and quick,
And akin to anaesthetic.

He fell to the floor and knew no
	more,
His passion extinct and dead.
He did not shout when his prick
	slid out,
Though it was stripped down to a
	thread.

Then Mexico Pete jumped to his feet
To avenge his friend's affront.
With a jarring jolt of his Blue Nosed Colt,
He rammed it up her c●●●!

He rammed it up to the trigger grip,
And fired it - two times three.
But to his surprise, she closed her eyes
And smiled in ecstasy.

S he jumped to her feet, with a
    smile so sweet,
'Bully," she cried, "for you!
Though I might have guessed that
    was the best
That you poor sod could do!"

"When next, my friend, that you
    intend
To sally forth for fun.
Buy Dead Eye Dick a sugar stick,
And yourself an Elephant Gun!"

"I'm going back to the frozen
   North,
Where pricks are hard and strong.
Back to the land of the frozen
   stand,
Where the nights are six months
long."

"It's as hard as tin when you put
   it in,
In the land where toffee is toffee!
Not a trickling stream of lukewarm
   cream
But a frozen, solid chunk!"

"Back to the land of the grinding
  gland,
Where the walrus plays with his
  prong.
Where the polar bear wanks off in
  his lair,
That's where they'll sing this
  song!"

"They'll tell this tale on the
  Arctic trail,
Where the nights are sixty below.
Where it's so damn cold that
  Johnnies are sold,
Wrapped up in a ball of snow."

"In the Valley of Death, with
   bated breath,
That's where they'll sing it, too.
Where the skeletons rattle in
   sexual battle
And rotting corpses screw."

"Back to the land where men are
    men,
Terra Bellicum!
And there I'll spend my worthy
    end,
For the North is calling - Come!"

So Dead Eye Dick and Mexico
    Pete
Slunk out of the Rio Grande.
Dead Eye Dick with his buggered
    prick,
And Pete - with no gun in his hand.

The End

If you've enjoyed this 'Freddie Farquar's 'Naughty but Nice!' Series title look out for others either in the book-shops now or in production.

Whatever the event, from Christmas and Easter to Father's Day or just *Any Day*, someone you know would *love* to receive a Freddie Farquar!

Freddie Farquar's
'Naughty but Nice!' Collection of:

Beastly but pointedly honest comments and opinions about Lawyers and assorted m'learned FRIENDS

NERDY anecdotes and things computer anoraks get their rocks off on